PLENTY

OF FISH

by

Millicent Selsam

With illustrations
by

Erik Blegvad

A Science I CAN READ Book

HARPER & ROW, PUBLISHERS
NEW YORK, EVANSTON, AND LONDON

PLENTY OF FISH

Library of Congress catalog card number: 60-5786

To

Lilian and Jonny

Here is Willy.

He wanted goldfish.

"Father," he said, "I want some goldfish.

I have the money to buy them.

Where do they sell goldfish?"

"Try the five and ten," said his father.

7

Willy went to the five and ten.

"Where are the goldfish?" he asked.

"Over there," a man said.

He looked for a fish tank.

But there was no tank.

The goldfish were in little plastic bags

hanging on hooks.

Willy was surprised.

Fish in plastic bags!

"How much for a fish?" asked Willy.

"Twenty cents each," the lady said.

"I want two, please," said Willy.

And he took the two little bags home.

"I got the fish, Father," he said.

"Where shall I hang them?"

"Willy," said his father,

"I forgot to tell you.

You need a fish bowl.

Here is money.

Go and buy one."

Willy went back to the five and ten.

He came home with a nice round bowl.

Willy put water in the bowl.

Then he opened the plastic bags

and the fish swam into the water.

"These goldfish are mine!" said Willy.

"I will feed them."

"What will you feed them?"

asked his father.

Willy thought.

"Can I feed them bread and butter?"

asked Willy.

"That won't do," said his father.

"A fish is not a boy.

Go back to the store.

Ask the lady

what the fish can eat."

14

Willy came back from the store.

"Fish eat fish food!" he cried.

"It comes in a little box.

Here it is."

His father opened the box.

"Oh," he said,

"so this is what goldfish eat."

16

"I want to feed my fish right now,"

said Willy.

He held the box over the bowl.

"Wait!" cried his father.

"Willy, wait!

Read what it says on the box."

"It says, 'Feed the fish a small pinchful

every day,'" said Willy.

"What is a pinchful?"

"As much as you can pinch

in your fingers," said his father.

Willy took a pinch of the fish food.

He held it over the bowl.

"Now let go," said his father.

The food dropped on the water.

"Now watch," said his father.

One goldfish came up to the top

and snap! the food went into its mouth.

The other goldfish came up

and snap! the food went into its mouth.

20

"Can I eat some fish food?" asked Willy.

"You won't like it," said his father.

Willy put some in his mouth.

"I like bread and butter better," he said.

"Father," said Willy, "it says on the box that the fish eat only once a day. I want to eat only once a day too!"

"All right," said his father.

"You ate once today.

You can eat again tomorrow."

"Yes," said Willy.

That night Willy said,

"Father, I'm hungry. I am not a fish."

"That's right," said his father.

"You are not a fish.

You have to eat more often."

And Willy sat down to dinner.

Willy liked to look at his fish.

He liked to see them

open and close their mouths.

"Why do they do that?" asked Willy.

"My fish open and close their mouths

all the time."

"They are breathing," said his father.

"Breathing?" said Willy. "Like this?"
and Willy opened and closed his mouth.
He sat there
and opened and closed his mouth
until he got tired.

25

Then Willy's father said,

"Willy, close your mouth."

Willy closed his mouth.

"Are you breathing?" asked his father.

Willy moved his head up and down

to say yes.

"Now hold your nose

and open your mouth," said his father.

Willy held his nose and opened his mouth.

"Are you still breathing?"

asked his father.

"Yes," said Willy through his nose.

"Now, Willy," said his father, "do this.

Close your mouth and see how long

you can hold your breath."

Willy held his breath for ten seconds.

Then he let go of his nose

and opened his mouth.

"Wow!" said Willy.

"It's good to breathe again."

29

"What are you breathing?"

asked his father.

"Air!" cried Willy. "I breathe air!

See! There's air all around me.

I can't see it.

30

"But it's there.

I know it's there!

When I hold my nose and close my mouth,

I can't get any air."

"Willy," said his father,

"do fish have air all around them

the way you do?

Did you really breathe like a fish

when you sat there

opening and closing your mouth?"

31

"No," said Willy.

He didn't say any more.

He just went back to look at his fish

swimming in the water.

Willy sat there and watched.

Then he walked to the bathroom.

He went to the sink

and turned the water on.

He turned it off when the sink was full.

Then Willy took a deep breath.

33

He held his nose
and put his face into the water.
He opened and closed his mouth
for a few seconds.
Then he came up for air.
Once more Willy put his face down
into the water.
Once more he opened and closed his mouth.
Then he came up for air again.

"Father," he called,

"come here! Come here!"

When his father came, Willy said,

"How can my fish breathe in the water?

I can't. I have to take a deep breath

before I put my face in the water.

And then I have to come up for more air."

"Willy," said his father.

"There is air in the water
of your fish bowl.

You cannot see it.

Just as you cannot see
the air around you."

Willy understood.

There was air in the water
of his fish bowl.

And somehow or other,
his fish could breathe that air,
even though he could not.

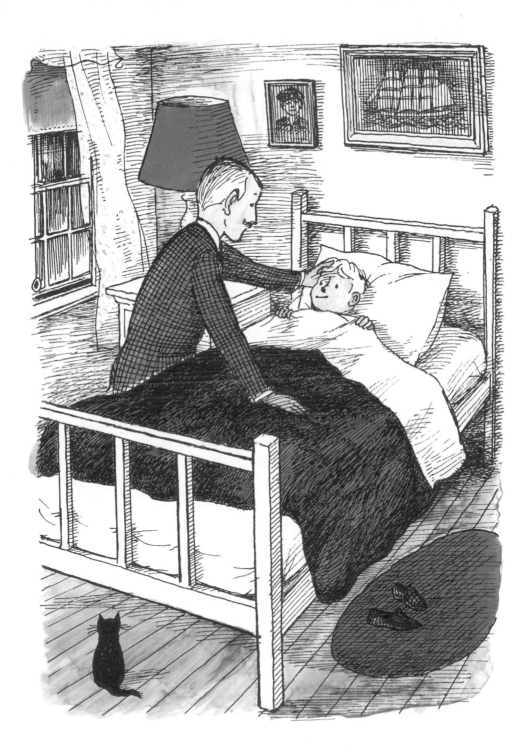

How did they do it?

Willy went back to watch his fish.

He watched one fish

open and close its mouth.

And then he saw something new.

The fish had a flap of skin

on the side of its head.

The flap was opening and closing too.

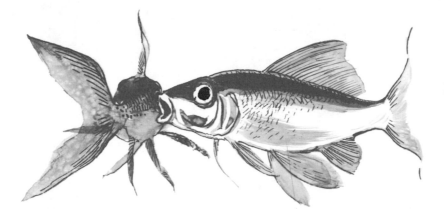

"Watch that fish," said Willy.

"That flap is opening and closing,
opening and closing."

"Yes, I see," said his father.

"When the fish opens its mouth,"
said Willy, "the water goes in.

Then it closes its mouth.

And the water goes right out

through the flap!

Maybe?"

That night Willy found a fish

on the kitchen table.

"Fish for dinner!" said Willy.

He opened the fish's mouth

and looked inside.

Then he opened the flap

on the side of the head

and looked in.

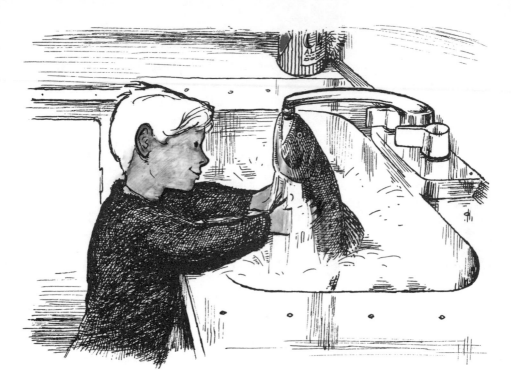

He turned on the water

in the kitchen sink.

Then he opened the fish's mouth

and let the water pour in.

He smiled!

The water was running out

behind the flaps!

He looked behind one of the flaps again.

There were soft red things inside.

Just then his father walked in.

"What have you got there?"

asked his father.

"Look," said Willy.

"Look under that flap."

His father looked.

"What are those red things?" asked Willy.

"They are gills.

They are full of blood," said his father.

"You were right, Willy.

The water does pass over the gills

under the flap.

The air in the water

goes into the blood."

"If I had more time," said Willy,

"I could have figured that out myself."

One day Willy went

to see his friend David.

David had goldfish too.

Two fish in a large tank.

There were green plants in the water.

"David," Willy said,

"those plants look nice in there."

"The man in the pet store

said I ought to get them," said David.

"He said they add something to the water—

something the fish breathe."

"David," said Willy,

"everyone knows fish breathe air.

What do the plants have to do with it?

Do plants make air?"

"I don't know," said David.

They sat there looking at the goldfish.

How can plants make air? thought Willy.

And then he saw something.

"Look, David," he cried.

There were little bubbles

all around the plant.

Little bubbles came off of the leaves

and floated up to the top.

"Bubbles! Bubbles of air!" said Willy.

"That's what they are.

Your pet man was right!

These plants are making air."

Willy and David walked around the corner
to the pet store.

"There's the man," cried David.

"Mister," said Willy,

"I need plants for my fish bowl.

I need them right now.

Could I pay you tomorrow?"

"What's the rush?" said the man.

"My fish need air.

I have two fish in one bowl

and no plants!" cried Willy.

"How do the fish look?" asked the man.

"Are they swimming all around?"

"They look fine," said Willy. "And yes,

they swim on the bottom, and on the top

and in the middle of the bowl."

"Then they're all right," said the man.

"You can wait. Your fish have air.

Some air goes into the water

at the top of the bowl.

"When you find the fish staying at the top,

you will know that you need more air

in the water.

Then you'll know that you need plants."

"We saw the bubbles of air

the plant makes," said Willy.

"You mean you saw the bubbles of *oxygen*," said the man. "That's the part of air that's important for breathing. That's the gas that plants give off when they're in the sun."

"Think of that!" said David.

"Oxygen! Oxygen!" Willy said to himself all the way home.

When he got home,

he ran to look at his fish bowl.

How could this be?

There were green plants in it.

He went to find his father.

"I got some plants

for your fish bowl, Willy,

and I'm going to let you figure out why."

Willy laughed. "I know why already."

He kissed his father and said thanks.

Then he went back to his fish bowl crying,

"Oxygen! Oxygen!"

When Willy came home from school

the next day,

he found something new in the fish bowl.

A large brown snail

was sliding along the glass.

Willy watched.

As it slid along, it cleaned up

the green slime on the glass.

"A vacuum cleaner for my fish bowl!"

said Willy.

When his father came home, Willy said,

"Father, you bought me a snail.

I watched it clean off

the side of the bowl."

"That's what I got it for, Willy,"

said his father.

"I didn't know about snails," said Willy.

"I will get a book about fish."

"Yes," said his father.

61

"And someday you can have a bigger bowl

and some more fish

and some more plants

and some more snails."

"Thank you, Father," said Willy.

"But I like my little fish bowl

and my two fish

and my two plants

and my snail.

I have plenty to watch."